Mole From the Meadow

MOLE
From the Meadow

written and illustrated by
BETTE J. DAVIS

Lothrop, Lee & Shepard Co. 🌷 New York

Sydney Anderson, Ph.D., Curator of the Department
of Mammalogy at The American Museum of Natural History,
read the manuscript for accuracy of facts.

Printed in the United States of America
Library of Congress Catalog Card Number: 78-116333
1 2 3 4 5 74 73 72 71 70

This book is especially for my mother and Jay

❧ Contents

❧1

Fallen Daffodils

Moles are destined to live in darkness. The industrious little animals dig, dig, dig underground, where they build their nests and obtain the food necessary for their existence. They are scarcely able to see. Yet, moles are marvelously adapted for the part nature has designed them to play in the world.

One such mole was presented to me in my New Jersey garden by my vigilant sheep dog, Musket. I often wondered what my dog would do if she ever managed to meet up with some wild thing. One day,

when the earth had turned to spring, I found out.

Musket barked. That's all she did. She yipped furiously at the furry animal feeling its way along the concrete walk in my backyard. It seemed the mole had lost its direction. From Musket's intense barking, I was certain, at first, that she had treed the Siamese cat that lived next door or finally knocked down the postman.

I dropped my gardening spade and ran to investigate the cause of the excitement. When I arrived on the scene, I became acutely aware of an unpleasant, musky odor that reminded me of the scent of a frightened skunk. The penetrating odor of the mole kept

Musket at bay, but as I came closer, she approached it cautiously. Probably born in the meadow in back, the mole had found its way into my garden. Having shown the rare treasure to me, Musket wagged her tail proudly. But she soon lost interest and bounded away to chase a squirrel up a budding dogwood tree.

Few people ever see a live mole. I felt privileged. I stooped down and gently picked up the seemingly helpless little thing. The mole was about six inches long—barely fitting in my hand—with mouse-colored, velvetlike fur, and an inch long naked pink tail. The mole was unharmed and very still. But it must have had fear in its heart, despite its outward calm.

The mole stirred in my hand while I looked at it carefully. There seemed to be no neck at all; its head was set so deeply between its shoulders. Hidden beneath the fur were two little openings for ears. The eyes were even smaller, like pinpoints. The forefeet were huge for the mole's size and ended in stout claws. The hind legs were much smaller, and I was surprised to see that they were webbed.

I remembered having read about a mole in one of my favorite storybooks when I was a child. This mole spent his time spring-cleaning his underground home with a brush and a pail of whitewash. He was an appealing little chap.

The mole I now held was quite real and wriggled slightly as I carried it back to the meadow. I found a place where I thought the mole would be safe from

any predator that might be lurking about—mainly my neighbor's Siamese cat. The mole made a sweeping movement with both forefeet as soon as it smelled the soil. It struggled in my hand, and the strength it showed was surprising. When I put the animal on the ground, it scrambled about frantically for a soft spot of dirt. Digging with its forefeet, the mole let turf and pebbles fly faster and faster. In just half a minute, the mole disappeared into the earth.

I stood there pondering for a moment. Obviously, the mole cared nothing for the sweet smell of air or the warm rays of the sun. What possible kind of life could the little creature have in the darkness of the underground? Why had the mole suddenly appeared in my garden this spring day? How long have moles been on earth or, rather, under it?

Absorbed in thought, I went back to the business of straightening my fallen daffodils. I knew now that it was my tiny visitor who had uprooted the flowers with its busy underground digging.

🌷2

The Mole's Hill

Later that day, the breeze turned chilly, and dark skies threatened April showers. I began to gather up the garden tools that were scattered around the backyard.

When I reached for the rose clippers, to my amazement, there was the mole again. It had a snoutful of crinkled leaves and was shuffling awkwardly through the grass. The leaves made it clear to me that by picking up the mole that morning, I had interrupted its errand.

The mole, of course, knew nothing of the interest it had created. It was completely absorbed in its own affairs. Intent only on getting the leaves to its underground nest, it crawled to a molehill—a mound of earth—nestled between the roots of an old sycamore tree that had been half shattered by lighting. I hadn't noticed the mole's hill before.

Making its entry, it kicked back the dirt to plug up the entrance hole, and for the second time that day, I watched the mole vanish into the earth.

If I could have followed the mole, I would have

found its home to be a veritable fortress, a complicated arrangement of runways and chambers. When a mole builds a burrow, it first loosens the soil by clawing and then pushes it upward to the surface. Tucking its snout between its legs, the mole spins over, slowly pushing the excavated earth into a pile, which becomes the molehill and entrance to the burrow.

Inside the molehill, the little animal scoops out dirt with its forefeet, shoving the loose dirt under its body and kicking it back with its hind feet. From time to time, the mole about faces in the tunnel and, bracing itself on one of its forefeet, shoves the excavated dirt through the tunnel with the palm of the

other foot. By using its hind feet, the mole propels itself and its load through the tunnel and then to the surface. This tunnel slants downward from the molehill, where the mole then constructs an oval chamber, about a foot wide. This is the mole's nest. Later, the mole will line it with dead grass and leaves. Next, the mole digs another tunnel leading up from the nest to a surface tunnel. This provides an exit for quick escape, in case the mole has to run for its life.

From the floor of the nest, the mole digs a permanent tunnel that may extend for many yards, branching in any direction. The dirt is packed along the sides, and the walls are made smooth by the friction of the mole's small body. The molehill is the entrance to the permanent tunnel, and no mounds are formed aboveground to reveal its existence. The permanent tunnel is about two feet under the surface of the ground.

In this tunnel, the mole remains during the cold weather. Here, too, earthworms bore down below the frost line. At various places along the permanent

tunnel, the mole burrows through the walls in search of food, whenever it feels the pangs of hunger—which is almost always. All winter long, the mole digs, gorging itself on earthworms.

The mole exists entirely on earthworms during the winter. Most of the insects it eats in the warm weather die with the summer. Before the insects die, a number of them deposit their eggs in the ground to be hatched the following spring. Some insects spend the winter rolled up in cocoons above the ground. Others migrate to warmer climates or hibernate under fallen branches or rocks.

While the mole continues diligently searching for food throughout the winter, the woodchuck sleeps soundly, curled up snugly below the frost line. The woodchuck builds its burrow for safety. Should the mole accidentally wander into the woodchuck's burrow, the mole is likely to ignore the sleeping rodent and go on with its digging. If the frost hardens the ground below the two-foot depth of the permanent tunnel, the mole simply digs deeper.

During periods of drought, when the sun has penetrated and hardened the ground, the mole again uses the permanent tunnel of its burrow. As the topsoil dries out, moisture seeps upward from the *water table,* keeping the earth around the tunnel moist and soft enough for the mole to continue its digging. The water table is the level below the ground that is completely saturated with water.

The surface tunnels are made chiefly to hunt for food. With the powerful strokes of its forefeet, the mole "swims" through the loose topsoil. Before digging deeper, the mole uses his snout to find a suitable spot to place its forefeet for the next stroke. Then the mole turns on its side, and pushes the excess dirt upward with either one of its forefeet. In this way it forms ridges known as surface tunnels. This clawing and tunneling is done very rapidly. The ambitious mole can dig one of its surface tunnels at the rate of twelve to fifteen feet in an hour.

During the warm weather, earthworms, which subsist on food plants, live near the surface, and larvae and insects also cluster around the roots of green plants. Thus the mole has a well-nourished fodder awaiting it in the loose topsoil. The mole may use the surface tunnels to forage only once. But if the ground is plentifully stocked with earthworms, larvae, and insects, these tunnels are used frequently and over a long period. People who live near meadows or gardens have seen the roof of a surface tunnel. The zigzag scar of cracked earth extending through my back lawn is one.

Each mole builds its own burrow. The elaborateness of the burrow depends on the individual mole.

One burrow may have more tunnels and chambers than another. Male and female moles have generally similar behavior, except, of course, that the female bears and raises the young.

Moles are unsociable and prefer to live alone. Occasionally, two or more male moles may occupy the same burrow system, but they tend to stay in different parts. Female moles almost never inhabit the same burrow. Sometimes, two males and one female may share one burrow, but this is rare.

The mole's burrow is often placed under a wall, fence, or under the roots of a tree. A most efficient engineer, the mole in my garden had built its burrow under the sycamore roots as an extra safeguard. I thought it rather daring, considering that a screech owl inhabited a hole in the same tree. So far, the mole and the owl had been unmindful of each other. I suspect the owl kept itself well stuffed with mice that lived in the meadow.

In just one night, my mole had dug a tunnel seventy-five feet long. Part of it was under my flower bed. I admired its mining ability, but its line of direction was somewhat annoying. During all of April and May, the little villain kept me busy "uprighting" lopsided daffodils and tulips. It became a contest to see if I could put the flowers straight faster than the mole could uproot them.

3

A Relic of the Past

By June, the grass had grown green and lush. Still, it did not hide those grotesque ridges of broken dirt that had branched out into various directions.

One evening I was mowing the back lawn, using a small tractor mower. It was a bumpy ride over that maze of ridges. I wondered if the mole could feel the vibrations of the mower. Was he in one of the tunnels? I had decided that my mole was a male. One can't easily tell with moles. But he was big, and male moles are bigger than females.

I did not quite know why I was concerned about the mole anyway. It is certain that moles were digging tunnels long before there were flower gardens. Moles have fended for themselves for a long, long time. Maybe on this very spot an ancestor of my mole had dug its tunnels about fifty million years ago.

I pictured the ancient mole in its secret passageway, shuddering under the thunderous tread of a gigantic beast. The earth around shook violently. Alert to even the slightest vibration, the tiny mole hunched its small but powerful shoulders, and dug its heavy claws into the dirt. Its strong ribs were braced to withstand pressure; and the prehistoric mole stood fast, waiting for the huge animal to pass overhead. The walls of the tunnel crumbled, and the mole blinked dirt from its eyes. Then, with incredible speed, it dug another passage in a different direction.

Moles have been around since the age of mammals, over sixty million years ago. Mammals—including man—are animals with hearts that pump warm blood into their bodies. They are also capable of producing milk to feed their young. The mole is a mammal. Mammals first appeared on earth after the extinction of dinosaurs, which had lived and thrived for millions of years before them. According to the laws of nature, all living things must adapt to their environ-

Unitatherium

ment or perish. Dinosaurs, for example, were unable to adapt to the change in temperature and the new forms of plant and animal life. And thus they gradually disappeared from the face of the earth.

The first mammals were mostly tiny animals, no bigger than rats or mice. Some took to the trees to avoid competition with the ground dwellers. In time, some insectivores—insect-eating mammals—became burrowing animals. As the years passed, thousands of years, some of the later mammals, such as the saber-toothed tigers, perished. They were trapped in tar pits or buried by molten lava and the debris of earthquakes. And, with the passage of time, still other animals have become extinct. But the mole lives on, a relic of the past, a living fossil.

Probably, moles have outlasted mightier beasts because moles are so small, and because they do live inside the earth. Its subterranean habitat has given the mole an advantage over creatures that walk the earth. The elaborate architecture of the burrow protects the mole from being attacked by predatory animals and offers shelter against some of nature's catastrophes. The fact that earthworms and insects are the mole's staple diet also accounts for its remarkable survival.

Underground, the absence of competition with other creatures makes it possible for the mole to continue its existence unmolested. Other animals that live in burrows come to the surface for food. Another conspicuous group of North American mammals that lives almost entirely underground is the pocket gopher of the West. Gophers dig tunnels, which they seldom leave, eating roots and stems as they go along. Sometimes they carry the roots away in their fur-lined cheek "pockets."

Through the centuries, the appearance of the mole has undergone some changes, but its habits have changed very little. After centuries of disuse, the eyes of most species have become almost invisible. The eyelids have fused together, forming a thin skin over the eyes. The mole can barely distinguish light from dark. Its external ears have also completely disappeared. Only two little holes at the sides of its head, which lead to the inner organs of hearing, remain.

Soft and thick as plush velvet, the mole's fur lies flat in any direction. If the fur were not so flexible, it would catch against the sides of the narrow burrow, and prevent the mole from backing out. When a mole goes in reverse, so does its fur, enabling it to scoot backward with ease. The fleshy, pink, little tail guides the mole on its backward journey through the blackness. The tapering hairs prevent particles of soil from adhering to the mole's fur.

In the advance of civilization, as man plowed fields

and cleared forests, making way for farms and cities, the habitats of many wild animals were destroyed. Undisturbed, the energetic little moles continued digging in the safety of the ground. Unless something unforeseen occurs, moles promise to subsist beneath the surface of the earth for a long time to come.

A sudden jolt of the lawn mower brought my thoughts back to the mole in my garden. He must have remained in his nest while I was mowing. There were no signs of him.

🌱4

Insectivores

There are several different species of moles. Plump and furry, all are skilled miners and members of Insectivora, the insect-eating order of mammals. Moles and shrews, the smallest of our mammals, have the largest populations in the North American group of Insectivora.

Moles are found in the Northern Hemisphere, both in the New World and the Old World. They must live in the soft, moist soil that earthworms occupy. Therefore, moles cannot exist in desert regions

Seven Species of Moles in North America

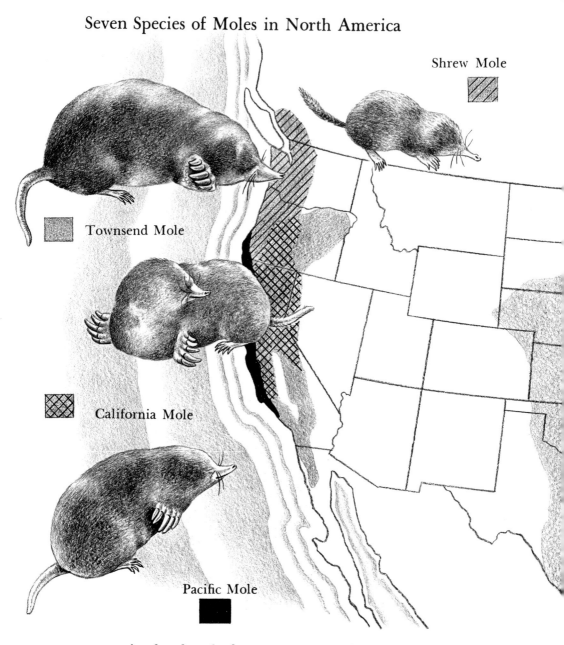

Shrew Mole

Townsend Mole

California Mole

Pacific Mole

or in the deeply frozen ground of the far north. Animals can thrive only in places having food, shelter, and the other necessities required for their existence.

Digging in the soil from southern Canada south-

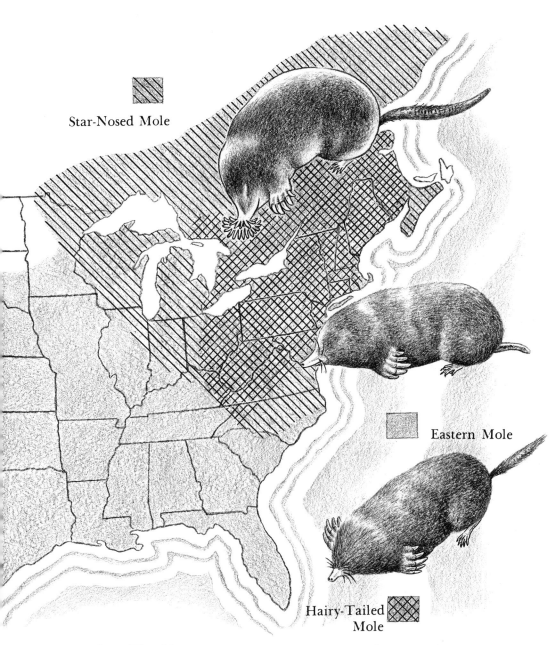

Star-Nosed Mole

Eastern Mole

Hairy-Tailed Mole

ward to Florida, eastern, or common, moles are our most familiar moles. Their scientific name is *Scalopus aquaticus*. The Latin word *aquaticus* means living in water. The eastern mole acquired this name

because of its webbed hind feet. The five toes of each
foot are linked by small areas of skin-covered tissue.
The eastern mole, however, in spite of its webbed
feet and all the water that surrounds it, is not
aquatic. The mole in my garden was an eastern mole.
I knew he was a most ambitious digger, but I wondered what would happen if he found himself in
water.

The first summer storm came. Claps of thunder
rattled in the sky. Driving rains soon beat against the
house and ran in rivulets down the windowpanes. In
the afternoon, the torrent turned to a slow, steady
drumming of warm rain. The rainstorm flattened
the tunnels, turning them into blurred streaks of
mud, and formed deep puddles in the backyard.

I began to worry about the mole. Suppose his
burrow flooded? I visualized the tiny creature strug-
gling for survival. I was relieved to know that all
moles can swim if it is absolutely necessary. Only in
lowlands are moles in danger of drowning from
floods. The rain stopped that evening, leaving the
air fresh and cool. The rhythmical song of the
crickets filled the summer night.

The next morning, when the sun came out again,
there was a new tunnel in the backyard. In fact,
there were two. In the earth below, my mole had
been very busy indeed—and very hungry.

❦ 5

The Mole's Menu

The mole has an enormous appetite. Each day it can easily devour its own weight in food. Digestion is rapid, and the mole has no way of storing food in its body. If deprived of nourishment, therefore, it would soon die, succumbing in less than twelve hours. Active night and day throughout the year in search of food, moles must eat huge quantities in order to get the energy to keep on searching for more food.

Fortunately, this tiny tiller of the soil was fash-

ioned in the right proportion to its appetite. Suppose
the mole in my garden had been the size of a lion—
and ate his own weight in food every day! I shivered
to think that if the ravenous mole weighed five hun-
dred pounds—instead of four ounces—it would be
the most ferocious beast in the world.

Moles have a habit of feeding at regular intervals.
Like most animals, they have a natural, or biological,
time clock. They may be found at work every day, at
four hour intervals, munching on worms or digging
for grubs, centipedes, spiders, and soft, and even
hard-shelled, insects. One little mole can consume
almost forty thousand insects and worms each year.

Moles cannot grasp anything with their claws.
They snatch up their prey in their mouths and chew
until their meals are swallowed. Between feeding
times, moles rest or sleep in their secluded tunnels.
Tired and full, a mole may stretch out and sleep on
its stomach, or snooze peacefully standing on all four
feet, its nose tucked beneath its chest. The mole may
slumber soundly in its nest or doze in a tunnel, the
front part of its body resting on a root or a stone.
Often, the mole's feet go through the motions of
digging, even when it is asleep.

A mole's senses of smell and touch are highly de-
veloped. With its snout, the mole can detect a delicate scent at a great distance. Sensitive hairs on its

Earthworms

front feet and tail supplement sight and hearing.
Leading from these sensory hairs, a series of nerve
trunks carry messages to the mole's brain. So great
is the mole's sensitivity to movement, it can feel the
tiny commotion of an insect tumbling in a distant
part of the tunnel. With quivering snout, the mole
then pursues the insect and catches it in a flash.

On another occasion, a mole may burrow its way to the underground nest of a yellow jacket family living under a log. Following their scent, the mole digs its way to the nest. Then, facing away from the nest, the mole begins clawing with its forefeet, throwing the dirt beneath its body and kicking it back with its hind feet. Hastening, in anticipation of a delicious meal, the mole forces dirt against the nest, until the insects inside are completely crushed. Then the mole turns around and digs its way into the nest and safely proceeds to devour both the young and adult insects.

Many gardeners mistakenly believe that moles eat the roots and bulbs of plants and flowers. The mole is not the culprit. Its tunnels, however, are often invaded by meadow mice that do eat roots and cause considerable damage in seedlings and roots of young plants. Sometimes, moles will stop to nibble on the planted grains of corn, wheat, and oats. But moles cannot exist on a steady diet of plant food. Only mice, rabbits, and other animals who live at a slower pace can survive on seeds and grasses. Moles must have meat, rich in protein and fat, to supply them with the energy needed to sustain their frantic pace. The life experiences of the voracious little mole consist mainly of digging in loose, moist earth, and eating the various worms and insects that make up its

Meadow Mouse

diet. Moles even eat trespassing mice, bones and all, if they haven't already had their fill of a dozen or more earthworms.

Earthworms surface in wet weather and emerge at night to feed on decaying bits of plants and animal matter. As twilight approaches, daytime animals return to their nests to sleep through the night. But with the shielding darkness, countless numbers of nocturnal animals come forth to feed. Leaves rustle as the tiny feet of mice, rats, and shrews scurry across the meadow. Cottontails hop carefully into clearings, sit erect, and listen for signs of danger. In the air hawks, bats, insect-eating nighthawks, flying squirrels, and owls hunt on soundless wings. Night also brings out the prowling animals—skunks, foxes, and weasels—who use the cover of the night to stalk their prey.

If my mole were to follow earthworms at night, he might meet any of these animals in the garden or meadow. I hoped there were enough insects and larvae to keep my mole in his underground tunnels.

All summer long, the mole lived, tunneled, and hunted under my garden. The evidence was obvious —tilted tiger lilies and leaning rosebushes. Sometimes, his tunnels would break paths through the grass, forming peculiar abstract designs. But a mole's life does not consist of only digging and eating. A little excitement is added—as I was about to witness.

Long-Tailed Weasel

6

My Mighty Mole

It was midmorning in October when I felt the slight "earthquake" under my feet. I stopped raking leaves to watch the roof of a tunnel vibrating violently from some kind of internal struggle. Although I didn't see the battle, I heard the hisses and squeals.

Suddenly, a black snake wriggled out of an exit hole. Writhing and lashing, it was more than two feet long. Evidently, in the limited space of the tunnel, the powerful snake had failed to coil itself around the mole. The mole must have dug his teeth into the reptile and slashed at it viciously. Torn and bleeding, the wounded snake had managed to escape from my mighty mole. If it hadn't escaped, the mole could have feasted until only fragments of the snake remained.

If the mole had been outside his tunnel, there would not have been a battle. The black snake could have slithered up to the unsuspecting bit of fur and swallowed him in no time. A speedster underground, the mole moves at a snail's pace above. I recalled that April afternoon when I had seen my mole shuffling clumsily through the grass. I had thought then that nature was cruel to have placed the mole inside the earth, away from all beauty. But how well nature knows what she does.

The surface adventures of moles are very risky, as the lives of all wild creatures are full of peril. Some animals must escape in order to live, while others must capture. Moles do some of each. The worms and other insects that moles feed on are powerless when a mole attacks. But moles, in turn, are helpless when assaulted by larger animals that prey upon small things. In the open, they become easy prey to predators. Their slowness above ground and their poor vision put them at the mercy of any enemy capable of capturing them.

Even underground moles are not entirely free

from danger. Skunks can dig into the dark hallways in search of a mole dinner. Weasels can creep into a mole's burrow, their small, slender bodies easily darting through the narrow tunnels. In the confines of the ground, however, moles have a chance of digging their way to safety. They have the ability of most mammals to move quickly in their environment.

Moles may come to the surface voluntarily on cloudy days or at night. In early spring, they must emerge to find leaves and grass for their nests, or possibly to seek mates if they have not found them underground. Searching uncertainly about for nesting materials or a mate, the mole cannot see a bird's shadow passing over the ground. The shadow becomes a diving hawk. The hawk swoops down on the helpless mole, grips it with its sharp talons, and airlifts it swiftly away. I've never seen a hawk in my part of New Jersey, but I do know predacious birds are around. Sparrow hawks and red-tailed hawks fly about the meadow. I've never seen the screech owl that lives in the sycamore either, and he's right in my backyard. I've certainly heard his wailing cry. One night, though, I saw a great horned owl flush out of the woods.

Sometimes, a mole's predator may be a crow or a cat mousing in the meadow. Venturing across the grass, the mole is unaware of the cat's padded paws

silently stalking the darkness. Suddenly, the cat pauses, pricks her ears, sees, and pounces on the soft mole with assured accuracy.

A dog or a fox does not actually have to see the mole, but may observe the ground rising as the mole passes through a tunnel. Leaping on the tunnel, the attacker pins the mole in the passageway. The predator, which may be a dog more dedicated to hunting than Musket, then digs out its quarry. Dogs are content to unearth and kill their tiny victims; they never eat moles. Some predators do not eat the mole because of its strong odor. Others dine contentedly on their catch. Weasels, skunks, and owls do not mind the mole's musky odor a bit.

Moles cannot defend themselves against most

Red Fox

predacious animals—or man. But if they have to, moles will savagely fight larger animals in their underground homes. Though their teeth are small, they are extremely potent weapons. As in other insectivores, the mole's teeth are sharply pointed, ably fitting it for its carnivorous diet. The teeth—thirty-six in the eastern mole—also enable the mole to sever roots that interfere with moving through the many underground tunnels.

Underground, moles fight as bitterly against each other as they do against other animals. This is particularly true of the males during the mating season in early spring. Woe to two males which happen to claim the same bride. They fight until one retreats in defeat from the battle. Most of the time the fight ends with the death of one of them. The victor often dines on the vanquished.

Somehow, I found it hard to believe that the velvet mole I had once held in my hand could fight so viciously. He had seemed so helpless then.

7

The Mole and Its Young

Winter frosts hardened the ground, and snow covered the molehill. The winds turned bitter, the cold became intense. Confident that my mole was safe from predators and winter frosts in his underground burrow, I forgot about him. January passed, and February brought a fine thaw.

It wasn't until March, when the crocuses pushed their heads impatiently through the melting snow, that I thought of the mole again. I looked out the kitchen window. The tunnels were gone. The small mound of earth between the sycamore roots had disappeared. I was a little saddened, but I accepted the fact that the mole had probably deserted my garden or finally met up with the screech owl.

The following Sunday, I was adjusting the screen door when I saw it—the bumpy stretch of earth. I never thought I would actually feel joy at seeing a broken strip of dirt scattered across the even lawn. I followed it straight to the molehill. This time, the mound rose between two large rocks next to the fence post.

Suddenly, without a hint of warning, a mole scudded through the top of the molehill. Covered with blood, the mole had certainly not surfaced by choice. Having escaped from the jaws of death, the mole clipped for a clump of grass as fast as its clumsy legs could carry it. It wasn't my mole. The fur was darker. Besides, I was sure that my mole would never retreat from a fight.

I waited and watched the molehill. Sure enough, his snout appeared, his teeth snapping with as much menace as a tiny defender could muster. He did not chase the other mole. He simply slid back into the molehill, kicking back dirt and covering the hole. Twice now, I had seen my mole eject an intruder from his molehill. How many he had actually dined on, I could only guess.

I knew what had happened. At least, I was fairly certain. It was mating time, and the two moles must have caught the scent of a female mole at the same time. Small wonder I hadn't heard them scuffling before I saw the dark mole bolt like a streak of furry lightning from the molehill.

The primitive drive to reproduce its own kind interrupts the mole's life of solitary seclusion. Squeaking and squealing, male and female both claw frantically through the underground tunnels, anxiously searching for each other. Spring is the time for courting and nest-building not only for the mole. Other wild animals are also procreating their species. The owl in the sycamore had acquired a mate. I could hear them wailing together. By now, probably two round, white eggs were in their nest.

The sounds of spring almost always begin with the liquid song of bluebirds. Then the bobolinks come back from their winter sojourn in Brazil, singing their rippling song as they fly across the meadow to their nests in the grass. I wonder what mysterious messenger whispers to them, telling them when and where to go.

Eagerly I watch for the meadow to come to life every spring. Today, I heard the woodchuck whistle as it emerged from its burrow for the first time after its deep winter sleep.

Bobolinks

Spring always starts slowly. Then suddenly all
nature wakens in a rush. Buds push open their
petals, trees unfurl their leaves, eggs hatch swarms
of insects or birds to crawl or fly about the meadow.
Seeds sprout into plants, sending the perfume of
clover and violets from the meadow.

During nest-building time, moles keep their bur-

Woodchuck

row entrances open, making it easier to carry back their nesting materials of grass and leaves. At all other times the burrow is kept closed.

Mating time is slightly different in the North than in the South. In the northern states, moles seek out their mates in March. Southern moles begin their courting in February, when the temperatures and weather are really like the early spring of March in the North.

After the wooing male has found his mate, the courtship is brief. He leaves her as soon as she has conceived their offspring. The baby moles are born six weeks later. The gestation period is the same length of time in both the North and South.

Returning to her solitary life, the female prepares her nest, turning it into a nursery for the babies she will soon bear. She fluffs up the grass and leaves, making the nest snug and soft. In April or early May, the female gives birth to from three to five moles. They are born blind, hairless, helpless, and they are about two-inches long. The mother curls her warm body around her young, suckling them and caring for them with great tenderness. If danger threatens, she maneuvers them with her snout to a safer place until all danger has passed. The mother must continue to eat—even more than she usually does—to supply milk for her babies. At intervals, she hurries down a tunnel, gobbles her food, and hurries back again to her infants. For a brief time, her children are more important to her than anything else.

The babies grow rapidly. By the time they are ten days old, they are furred miniatures of their parents. They begin to crawl about the nest, chirping and playing as all baby animals do. When the young

moles are about a month old, their mother drives them off to fend for themselves. They set out in different directions to begin their solitary lives.

At two months, the moles are nearly full grown. The males are slightly larger than the females. Adult moles weigh about three or four ounces. When spring comes again—about ten months later—the young moles will be ready to breed. Possibly, the dark mole who had just bolted from the molehill was my mole's offspring of last year. I was reluctant to think my mole was such a rowdy father. But that is the way of a mole.

I wondered if he had started a new family, and if I would see him again.

8

Friend or Foe

Daffodil time had come again, and I was putting my garden in order.

"Got him! Detestable little devil!" I heard my neighbor say from the garden next door.

Another mole had been introduced to death by the flat side of a gardener's spade. Try to tell someone whose beautiful lawn has been disfigured by a mole's tunnels that this underground mammal is beneficial, and the answer will probably be similar to the one I got.

"Beneficial? Don't make me laugh!"

Without meaning to, industrious little moles make enemies wherever they go. Not only is the sight of molehills on a beautiful lawn unsightly, the tunnels and mounds make mowing more of a chore than it already is. Besides, the mole has the annoying habit of building its tunnels below the rows of young farm and garden crops. It loosens and injures some choice plants while probing for grubs amongst the roots. If the roots are broken, they cannot absorb the minerals and water they need from the soil. Then the entire row may dry up.

Most wild animals help to maintain the balance of nature. Predatory attacks are among the most effective means of preventing a species from multiplying too fast. Unmolested, the descendants from just one pair of meadow mice would soon overrun the world. Fortunately, meadow mice are food for many birds and animals—owls, hawks, skunks, foxes, weasels, black snakes, and cats. When people kill hawks and owls, they reduce the exterminators of the meadow mice. Left free from predators, mice multiply and eventually destroy grass, grain, orchards, and almost every other kind of plant that is necessary to man. The damage meadow mice do amounts to millions of dollars every year. A region that is stripped of its predatory birds invariably becomes infested with rodents.

Moles have their own special role in maintaining the balance of our natural environment. Most farmers and gardeners unite in a war to destroy the mole. Harpoon, choker, and scissor-jaw traps are some of the devices used to exterminate moles. Unwittingly, the farmers kill one of their best allies in the culture of plants and flowers. I explained to my skeptical neighbor that the good the mole does is far greater than any damage it may innocently cause to crops.

The mole's tunnels prevent topsoil from becoming mud by draining the rain through the network of tunnels. In dry soil, the burrows act as small irrigation systems, permitting the rain to be more evenly distributed. The mole's digging brings subsurface soil to the top. By regularly turning subsoil and carrying decayed vegetation and other organic substances below the surface, moles contribute to the natural building up of soil fertility. This enables the soil to produce crops of fruit, vegetables, flowers, and other plants. The earth is more productive because for countless generations moles have dug their tunnels. These steadfast toilers have helped enrich the soil.

By now, my neighbor was sitting on the steps, listening earnestly. Pointing to the flourishing fruit trees, I continued to expound the virtues of the mole. Perhaps the most important part the mole plays in

the ecological balance is that it depends on ground .
insects for food in order to live. Moles eat huge
quantities of Japanese beetles as well as the larvae
from which they develop. Moles consume enormous
amounts of cutworms, wireworms, grubs, and other
insect pests. These pests thrive only because man has
provided them with a bountiful food supply. The
simple act of planting crops changes the natural environment and supplies insects with food.

When natural surroundings are undisturbed, they
maintain a balance between living things and their
food supply. Planting crops, building cities, and
making other changes are necessary for man to survive and progress. But when man destroys plants and
animals for his immediate needs, he upsets nature's
delicate balance and endangers his environment.

Plowing a field disturbs the habitat of wild creatures which would, if undisturbed, eat destructive insects. The crops, in turn, increase the food supply for
these insects, enabling them to thrive and multiply.
Pesticides must then be used to destroy the noxious
insects in order to preserve the plants. But at the
same time, pesticides kill useful insects—bees and
wasps, for example—that pollinate plants and lady-
bugs that destroy plant-eating insects, such as aphids,
which live by sucking sap from the leaves of plants.
Spraying poisons may kill other wildlife as well.

1. Japanese Beetle
2. Japanese Beetle Larva
3. May Beetle Larva (Grubs)
4. Wireworms
5. Cutworm

Were it not for the mole's insatiable appetite for insects, even more powerful pesticides would have to be used.

"Moles are very useful citizens," I concluded. "Even if they do some harm by their tunneling and foraging, they are far more useful than destructive. They should not be destroyed without good reason."

My neighbor was really feeling contrite about his thoughtless act. I had convinced him that this prehistoric survivor was nature's most serviceable creature in the shadowy underground world.

A mole has an active, but short life. It may live from one to three years, depending on how lucky it is. I wondered if this was my mole's second or third year. What really interested me was whether or not he had survived the mating season. Had he gone the ways of his ancestors? Was he decomposing in the ground, returning minerals back to the earth, maintaining the soil fertility even in death?

Gathering clouds covered the sun, and the sky became as dark as night. But I persevered in the chore of weeding my garden. Musket was contentedly lying nearby. Suddenly, she sat up, staring intently toward the meadow.

There, on the top of the world, the mole stood very still, as if he were listening to the wind. His snout was stuffed with crinkled leaves. Musket didn't bark this time. It was as if she knew what I knew. She had accepted the mole from the meadow as a member of the household.

❧ Suggestions for Further Reading

Arlton, A. V., "Ecological Study of the Common Mole," *Journal of Mammalogy.* vol. 17, 4:73–98.

Bates, Marston, *Ecology.* Prentice Hall, Englewood Cliffs, New Jersey, 1961.

Carrington, Richard, *The Mammals.* Time-Life Books, New York, 1963.

Colbert, Edwin H.,*Dinosaurs.* E. P. Dutton, New York, 1961.

Mattheissen, Peter, *Wildlife in America.* Viking Press, New York, 1959.

Milne, Lorus Johnson, *Ecology.* Prentice Hall, Englewood Cliffs, New Jersey, 1967.

Morris, Desmond, *The Mammals—A Guide to the Living Species.* Harper & Row, New York, 1965.

Shoemaker, Lois Meir, *Mammals of New Jersey.* New Jersey State Museum, Trenton, New Jersey, 1962.

❧ Index

Page numbers in italics denote illustrations.